Folens

eginning LANGUAGE WORK

Contents

Where Does it Come From?

Did you ever look at something and ask: Where did it come from? How does it grow? Everyone knows what a raisin looks like but does anyone know where it comes from or how it grows?

Believe it or not a raisin begins its life as a grape. You all know what a grape looks like, but can you imagine it turning into a raisin? How does this happen?

Grapes grow in France and in many other hot countries. They grow in bunches on small bushes called vines. The grapes become plump and juicy under the warm sun.

Some of the grapes are picked and laid out on wooden trays. They are left outside where the hot sun shines down on them. Slowly the sun dries up the juices and water that are in the grapes. Soon the grapes become dried up and wrinkled. They turn a brownish-black colour. The grape has now become a raisin.

After this the raisins are collected and taken to a factory. They still have their grape stems at this stage but in the factory these are taken off by special machines. The raisins are washed and then dried. They are then ready to be packed and shipped out to places all over the world.

Next time you help to make a cake you'll know where the raisins come from!

A **Answer these questions.**

    1. How does a raisin begin its life?

    2. In what country do grapes grow?

    3. What are vines?

    4. What kind of weather do grapes like?

    5. When the grapes have been picked what does the sun do to them?

    6. What happens to the stems on the raisins?

B **Write true or false for these sentences.**

    1. A raisin is a huge fruit.

    2. A raisin begins its life as an apple.

    3. Grapes grow in France.

    4. Grapes grow on bushes.

    5. The grapes are laid out on wooden trays.

    6. The grapes turn a bluish-grey colour.

C **Write the words in a-b-c order. Which word comes first?**

raisin	grape	vine	factory	tray	sun

D **Write about how a grape becomes a raisin. Use your own words.**

5

A **Write the missing letters in these ai words. Put them into sentences.**

1  _ai_	**2**  _ai_	**3** 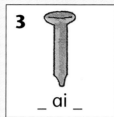 _ai_	**4**  _ai_	**5**  __ai_

B **Choose the correct word for each sentence.**

1. I hope I don't *(fall, fail, file, life)* my test.
2. I hurt my hand and the *(pain, pan, pane, pine)* was awful.
3. I cannot *(wait, waist, wire)* for the holidays.
4. The *(made, mate, maid)* made the beds.
5. I am going to *(pain, pant, paint)* the house red.
6. The wine left a *(stone, stain, saint)* on the cloth.

C **Write the correct oa word.**

1  goat boat	**2**  soap goat	**3** 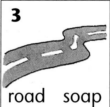 road soap	**4** 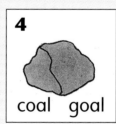 coal goal	**5**  coat goal
6  oak oats	**7**  loan load	**8**  toast toad	**9**  toad oats	**10**  coast roast
11  road roast	**12**  foal float	**13**  toast stoat	**14**  goal coal	**15**  goat goal

A **Choose the correct ea word. Write it. Make sentences.**

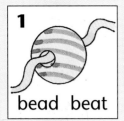
1 bead beat

2 team meat

3 flea leaf

4 tea eat

5 beak bean

6 dear read

7 lead leaf

8 flea heal

9 seal steam

10 steal steam

11 dream dear

12 cream real

B **Write the missing ee words for these sentences.**

1. I'm going to Spain next (wake, week, weed).
2. I can (peck, pale, peel) this orange in one go.
3. I will (meet, meat, meal) you at the bus stop.
4. I have to (week, wide, weed, weep) the garden.
5. The (deer, reed, dear) is in the park.
6. I have (been, bore, bone) waiting for you.
7. My grandad likes a pint of (been, bore, beer).
8. They had to (flare, feel, flee) from the town.
9. The grass is very (greedy, green, grease).
10. I have to (sweet, seed, sweep) up the leaves.
11. The (shear, sheep) have to get their fleeces sheared.
12. My hand is starting to (bleat, bead, bleed).
13. I was tired but I couldn't (sheep, sleep, steep).

7

Queen of the Pirates

Almost 500 years ago a daughter was born to Owen and Margaret O'Malley. They called their new baby Grace. Grace O'Malley was to become one of the most famous women in Irish history.

The O'Malleys were a rich and powerful seafaring family. They owned many fine castles in Mayo and in other places in the west of Ireland. They also owned a fine fleet of ships. Owen O'Malley was an Irish chieftain with long hair and his daughter Grace looked very like him.

From an early age Grace wanted to go with her father and brother on their sailing trips. However, she was always told that she could not because she was a girl.

One day Grace decided that she couldn't stand being left at home any longer. She went off and cut her lovely long hair and put on some boy's clothes. She then went up to her father and said, "Now will you take me with you?" He was shocked when he saw her shaved head but agreed to take her with him. In fact this is how Grace got the name 'Granuaile' which means 'bald Grace' in Irish.

Grace went on to become the bravest and best-known pirate on the west coast of Ireland. Her clever ideas and daring brought her riches and success. She was known for the way her ships seemed to appear out of nowhere and attack. Grace loved the exciting life of a pirate but she was also very good at business. Her fleet of ships was always laden with goods from distant lands.

At one time Grace faced a problem. A powerful man called Sir Richard Bingham was trying to stop her ships from trading. He had also put her son in prison. Grace decided to go to see the Queen of England to try to make a deal with her. Grace O'Malley, the pirate queen, met the Queen of England in September 1593. Between the two of them they sorted out the problem and Grace got what she wanted.

A **Answer these questions.**

1. What were Grace's mother and father called?
2. What kind of family were the O'Malleys?
3. Where did they live?
4. Who did Grace look like?
5. What did Grace want to do?
6. What did Grace have to do to join her father and brother?
7. Why did Grace have to change? Do you think this was fair? Write two sentences to explain.
8. Why do you think the story is called 'Queen of the Pirates'?

 B **Read 'Queen of the Pirates' again and find the paragraphs with these words in them. Write down their meanings.**

seafaring, chieftain, laden, trading
Check your answers in a dictionary.

C **A fact is something which is true. Fiction is made up.**

Do you think 'Queen of the Pirates' is a story which has facts in it or is it fiction? Why?

D **Write about the meeting between the Queen of England and Grace.**

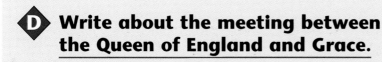

Write as if you were Grace. Begin: In 1593 I met the Queen of England.

A **Write a sentence for each ew word.**

1. few
2. new
3. flew
4. grew
5. stew
6. chew
7. crew
8. drew
9. threw
10. screw

I have only a few sweets!

B **Find these oo words in the wordsearch.**

roof
fool
tool
food
moon
loot
zoo
boot
pool
spoon
shoot
broom
balloon

D	S	R	J	K	F	W	P	S	P	O	O	N	D	E
Q	K	R	C	X	U	Y	B	N	G	F	L	D	S	B
V	C	E	W	S	L	H	G	C	X	S	O	Y	T	A
L	V	G	R	O	O	F	S	A	N	O	H	L	R	L
M	O	O	N	F	C	O	S	L	H	X	T	O	D	L
C	U	O	E	F	X	O	E	S	Z	X	Z	O	O	O
U	B	G	T	O	O	L	X	F	R	Z	A	N	R	O
Y	P	W	R	O	F	G	Y	R	E	X	L	Y	B	N
W	U	G	B	D	A	B	R	O	O	M	S	G	T	V
A	P	O	O	L	F	T	R	S	B	O	O	T	R	S
H	I	D	O	S	R	S	B	H	P	R	D	X	K	H
G	S	O	C	M	J	S	P	A	Q	S	H	O	O	T
Q	L	O	O	T	U	I	I	O	T	D	V	I	P	K
B	R	V	H	J	P	I	M	D	O	D	E	W	Q	I

C **Choose four of the above words and draw pictures of them.**

Write a sentence about each picture.

A **Choose the correct words and write them down.**

to two too   blue blew   made maid   hear here   road rode

B **Match the words in list 1 to words in list 2.**
They are linked by meaning. Write them down.

see	two
no	look
sea	fruit
pair	can't
know	water
pear	understand

C **Read this and write down the correct words.**

(*One/Won*) day the (*break/brake*) on Jack's bike did not work.
He fell off and hurt his (*heel/heal*).

The (*pain/pane*) made him
(*groan/grown*).

It took a (*weak/week*) to
get better.

His dad said he
(*mite/might*) get the bike
mended.

His brother said that he
(*would/wood*) (*by/buy*) Jack a
(*knew/new*) bike for his birthday!

11

A **The oo is missing from the words in the picture. Write the words in your book.**

Say the words.

B **Write sentences about the picture. Use oo words.**

Read your sentences.

C **Now read this.**

Write the words with **oo** and the words with **u**. Underline the sounds.

Pull on your woolly jumper and put your foot in that sock!

Look! A bull in a china shop!

D **Write the words in the bag in two lists, oi and oy.**

boil	joy	spoil
Roy	Leroy	join
noise	coin	boy
oil	toy	cowboy

E **Write out these sentences, putting in the missing letters oi or oy.**

1. I have a friend called Ler__ and another called R__.
2. If you b__l the egg too long you will sp__l it.

A **Write the words in two lists ow and ou.**

hound brown found sound cow flower town
shower south cloud count frown clown

B **Write down the correct word.**

1	2	3	4
flower/sound	hound/frown	count/town	cloud/clown

  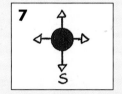 

5	6	7	8
found/clown	cow/south	brown/south	shower/found

 C **Read this poem. Write down all the words
with ar in them. Underline the sound.**

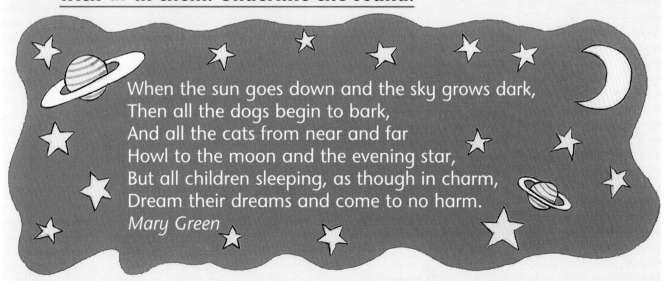

When the sun goes down and the sky grows dark,
Then all the dogs begin to bark,
And all the cats from near and far
Howl to the moon and the evening star,
But all children sleeping, as though in charm,
Dream their dreams and come to no harm.
Mary Green

D **Match the words that rhyme and write them down.
Choose two words and write sentences or a poem.**

parts   far   farm   dark
charm   lark   darts   car

One/More Than One

A **Look at the example then change the words to mean 'more than one'.**

● We sometimes add an **-s** to make a word mean 'more than one'.

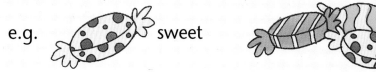

e.g.   sweet   sweets

Add an -s.

boat	table	cup	car	book
paper	kitten	ghost	pencil	chair
giant	bag	horse	coat	field

B **Look at the example then change the words to mean 'more than one'.**

● When we change some words to mean 'more than one', we add **-es**.

e.g.   dress   dresses

Add -es.

witch	ditch	wish	fox	mass
press	box	pass	brush	class
dish	branch	match	patch	stitch

C **Look at the example then change the words to mean 'more than one'.**

● When we change some words to mean 'more than one', we change **-f** or **-fe** to **-ves**.

e.g.   calf   calves

Change -f or -fe to -ves.

calf	leaf	wolf	wife	sheaf
elf	knife	hoof	thief	loaf
shelf	half	life	yourself	

Animal Families

 A **Look at these animal families. Read and copy down the first one. Write the others yourself.**

1. look    looking    looked

2. play 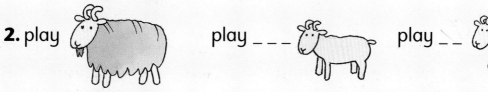   play _ _ _    play _ _

3. stay    stay _ _ _   stay _ _

B **Sometimes we drop the e. Read and copy the first one. Do the others yourself.**

4. joke    joking    joked

5. bake    bak _ _ _    bak _ _

6. rake   rak _ _ _    rak _ _

C **Write out the sentences. The first has been done for you.**

Mr Brown played with the lambs.
Mrs Brown look___ for the hens.
Mr Green bak___ bread.
Mrs Green rak___ the leaves.

15

Witches

Sometimes when we think of Hallowe'en we also think of witches. Many years ago, most people believed in witches. They also believed that Hallowe'en was a time when witches were at their most wicked. Some people even went so far as to light fires to try and burn the witches as they flew by on their broomsticks.

In those days, witches were often hunted down. When they were caught they were sometimes taken to a bonfire and burned. Of course, they were not witches at all. They were women whom some people wanted to get rid of. These people would tell lies about a woman and make others believe that she was a witch. Many women were killed when they had done nothing wrong.

Sometimes when a woman was accused of being a witch she would be lowered into the local river or pond. A special chair was built in order to do this. If the woman floated, it meant she was a witch and she would be burned to death. If she didn't float, in other words if she drowned, it meant that she wasn't a witch. Either way she couldn't win. Either way she died.

It was believed that witches had amazing powers and that they got this power from the devil. People thought that witches could fly on broomsticks and change themselves into animals.

It was also believed that the wood from the rowan tree would keep you safe from the power of the witches. If a witch came near you, all you had to do was wave a branch of this tree and you would be saved!

Have you ever heard of Joan of Arc? She was burned because people said she was a witch. She lived in France about 600 years ago and at that time the French were at war with the English. Joan led the French army to many victories against the English. Eventually she was captured by the English and thrown into prison. The English wanted to get rid of her so they accused her of being a witch. Without even getting a chance to defend herself she was burned at the stake on 30 May 1431.

A **Write answers to these questions.**

1. Why did people light fires at Hallowe'en?

2. Why did people hunt 'witches'?

3. What happened when a 'witch' was caught?

4. How was a 'witch' lowered into water?

5. What did it mean if she floated?

6. What did it mean if she didn't float?

7. Why could the 'witch' never win?

8. From where did people think 'witches' got their power?

9. Why do you think some people wanted to believe in 'witches'?

 B **Write about Joan of Arc. Finish these sentences.**

1. Joan of Arc lived ...

2. She led the French army to ...

3. The English ...

4. They wanted to ...

5. In the end Joan of Arc was ...

C **Find out how you make a Hallowe'en pumpkin.**

Explain in three steps, like this:

First ...
Next ...
Finally...

abc

A **Say the sounds of these consonants.**

b c d f g h j k l m n p q r s t v w x y z

B **Say and write out these words and underline the consonants.**

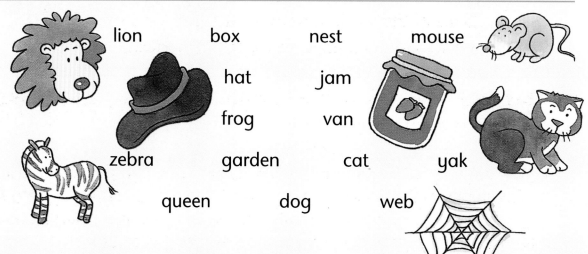

lion   box   nest   mouse

hat   jam

frog   van

zebra   garden   cat   yak

queen   dog   web

C **Say the rhyme and write it down.**

Remember!
a e i o u
are the vowels for me and you.

D **Write out these sentences and underline the vowels.**

1. I like pears.
2. You like apples.
3. We love sweets!

Capital Letters

Do you remember when to use capital letters?

- At the start of a sentence.
- When you write 'I'.
- For names of people and places, e.g. Pam is in Spain.
- For personal titles, e.g. Miss, Mr.
- For days of the week, months of the year and special days.
- For headings, book titles and special emphasis.

A **Read this piece. Copy it and write the missing capital letters.**

__ello! __y name is __elen.

__very __uly we go to visit my big sister __am. __he lives in __rance with her husband __aul. __hey have two children called __icola and __om. __am is expecting another baby in __ctober. __hey come over to visit us at __hristmas and sometimes for __aster as well.

__ell I'd better go now, it's __unday evening and I have to write an essay on the book '__anny the __hampion of the __orld'.

B **Write a few sentences using the words in the boxes.**

| May | Sunday | Easter | Spain | Friday | Karen |

C **Copy these sentences. Fill in the blanks with words of your own.**

1. My favourite special days of the year are _____ and _____ .
2. The months I like best are _____ and _____ .
3. The girls' names I like most are _____ and _____ .
4. I would love to go to _____ for a holiday.
5. My birthday is in the month of _____ .
6. The days of the week I like best are _____ and _____ .
7. My favourite book is _____ .

The Dove and the Ant

Have you ever wondered where the saying 'One good turn deserves another' comes from? Read on and find out.

One very hot day, a little ant was rushing along. Suddenly he stopped. His three pairs of legs screeched to a halt. He found himself beside a stream.

"Why am I rushing along at such speed?" he said to himself. "Why don't I stop and have a nice cool drink? It's a hot day and I am very thirsty."

Suddenly he heard a voice coo from above. It was the voice of a beautiful white dove that was perched on the branch of a tree.

"Little ant," the dove cooed, "why don't you get a drink from the stream?"

The little ant looked at the lovely cool stream that was running close by.

"What a good idea," he said.

"Just be careful you don't fall in," warned the dove.

The ant hurried down to the edge of the stream and began to drink. He was almost finished when a sudden gust of wind tossed him into the water. The poor little ant could not swim and was in danger of drowning.

"Help! Help!" he shouted.

The dove saw what was happening and tried to think of how she could help. Suddenly she had an idea. She grabbed a leaf from the tree and flew down to the ant. She dropped the leaf beside him.

"Climb onto the leaf," she shouted.

The ant did as he was told and scrambled onto the leaf. The leaf floated safely to the edge of the stream and the little ant fell onto the bank.

"Thank you, kind dove," he gasped. "Someday I will repay you."

A few days later, the dove was flying through the forest. The ant was hurrying along the ground as usual. He saw the dove up above him and was about to wave when he saw something else. It was a hunter laying a trap for the dove.

The dove did not see the hunter and flew down towards the trap. The little ant tried to think of how he could save her. Suddenly he had an idea. He threw himself against the hunter's bare ankle and bit it hard with his sharp teeth.

The hunter howled in pain. The dove was very close to the trap but she heard the hunter's howl just in time and knew she was in danger. She saw the ant beside the hunter and his trap and she knew that the little fellow had saved her.

A Write these sentences in order, to tell what the dove did for the ant.

She gave the leaf to the ant and he floated to safety.

The dove grabbed a leaf from a tree.

The dove told him to have a drink from the stream.

A gust of wind tossed the ant into the water.

He stopped and thought he would have a drink.

The little ant was rushing along.

B Write six sentences to tell what the ant did for the dove.

C What can we learn from the story of 'The Dove and the Ant'?

Write down your answer.

D When did you do a good turn for someone?

Write three sentences about it.

E Write sentences that include these words.

1. screeched   **2.** scrambled

3. tossed   **4.** perched

5. wondered   **6.** hurried

F Write a story for this saying.

'Look before you leap'

Begin by saying ... One day, not so long ago ...

Change the Story

 Talk about it.

You have read the story 'The Dove and the Ant'. The poor little ant was drowning and the dove saved him. However, what if the dove was not a kind dove?

What would have happened if she had decided not to help the ant?

Would the ant have saved himself?

Would someone or something else have saved him?

If he had saved himself, would he have tried to get revenge on the dove? How?

 Change the story. The first line is done for you.

Suddenly a gust of wind tossed the little ant into the stream.
The dove ...

 Draw a picture for your new story.

A Hibernating Hedgehog

A hibernating hedgehog,

Woke up to greet the spring,

He'd set the alarm for half-past May,

But he hadn't heard it ring.

In fact he'd gone and overslept,

A silly thing to do,

Not only had he missed the spring,

He'd missed the summer too.

Martin Honeysett

 **Write a short poem or story about
a bear who hated hibernating.**

Nouns

● A noun is the name of a person, place or thing, e.g. Sharon, Spain, dog.

 Look at these nouns.

Carol

Paris

horse

house

 Write out the sentences below and underline the nouns.

1. Fred the goldfish lived in France.
2. Carol lived with her granny in a small house in Wales.
3. Sammy is a fat seal who will only eat fishfingers.
4. My dog George followed our car down the road.
5. Our cat Fluffy will only drink coffee.

C **Choose a suitable noun for each sentence.**

1. (*Rover, Spot, Karen, Tom*) is a nice name for a girl.
2. The Eiffel Tower is to be found in (*London, Paris, water*).
3. The swift (*horse, tadpole, worm*) jumped the fence.
4. I live in a lovely (*wormery, den, house, kennel*).
5. I am sitting on a comfortable (*table, press, chair, video*).
6. I am going to (*Mars, Glasgow, school, hospital*) for my holiday.

A **Draw pictures for these words. Write the words. Ring ch and sh in each word.**

ship   chimney   sheriff   church

B **Read these 'silly' words. Write some of your own.**

shud   shem   chank   chof   shing   chesh   shumpy

C **Write the missing letters, ch or sh.**

1 _ _ ed

2 _ _ ildren

3 _ _ amrock

4 _ _ ips

5 _ _ icken

6 _ _ ell

7 _ _ est

8 ben _ _

9 bu _ _

10 _ _ op

11 _ _ elf

12 wat _ _

13 fi _ _

14 tor _ _

15 bun _ _

16 _ _ estnut

25

A **Choose f or ph to complete the words. Write out the full answers.**

1  _ ish	**2**  _ otograph	**3**  _ rog	**4**  li _ t	**5**  tele _ one
6  _ ox	**7**  ele _ ant	**8** 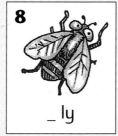 _ ly	**9**  dol _ in	**10**  gi _ t

B **Look at the pictures. Name each one aloud. Make two lists: words that begin with wh and words that do not.**

1 	**2** 	**3** 	**4** 	**5** 

C **Many question words begin with wh. Read each of these and then put them in sentences.**

Why?	When?	Where?	Who?	What?	Which?

D **The letters that complete each word are jumbled. Write them in the correct order with th first and read the word.**

1 mbu 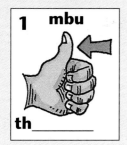 th_____	**2** ron  th_____	**3** chat  th_____	**4** dear  th_____	**5** lmeib 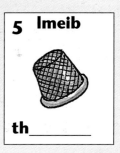 th_____

A **Write out the following putting in air. Read them to a friend.**

1

A h__y monster

2

A p__ of shoes

3

An old rocking ch__

4

At the f__

5

Up in the ___

6

Upst__s, downst__s

B **Now do the same with these, putting in are.**

1

The school c___taker

2

A r___ jewel

3

I d___ you!

4

A jumping h___

5

Take c___

6

Bew___ of the dog!

Be ---- of the dog

C **Write these out. The first has been done for you.**

1

Wear and tear

2

A teddy _____

3

A green _____

D **We often use where and there when we write.
Finish the answers to these questions in your book.**

1. Where is the teddy bear? There, in the ...
2. Where is your chair? There, by the ...
3. Where is your fare? There, on the ...

The Magic Oak Tree

 Talk about it.

- What can you see in this picture?
- Describe everything carefully.
- What are the men going to do?
- What do you think will happen?
- Will the animals or birds help?
- Will the rabbit frighten the horse?
- Will the cart roll into the river?
- Will the big tree cover the men with leaves?

 Write what you think will happen.

- Remember to use sentences.
- Remember to use capital letters.

A **Write the words in the box in three lists or, oor and aw. Say the words.**

sport	poor	claw	corner	fork
floor	saw	jaw	door	dawn horse
straw	torch	draw	crawl	morning

 B **Make words and write them out in your book. Say them.**

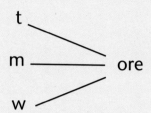

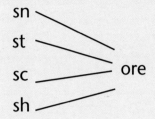

C **Which word fits? Write these out correctly and read them.**

August	sauce
autumn	saucer
	caught

1. cup and _____
2. summer and _____
3. the month of _____
4. chips and _____
5. _____ out!

D **Read this sentence. Write down the words with the au sound.**

The teacher taught my naughty little daughter to read.

E **What sound do the words on this page make?**

The Salty Sea

Have you ever swum in the sea? Have you ever swallowed a mouthful of sea water? What did it taste like? Yes, it tasted salty. Read on and find out why.

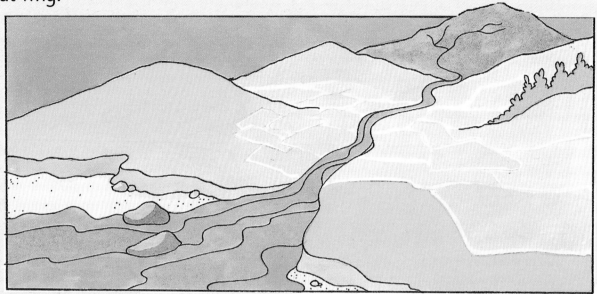

Rivers have been pouring their water into the sea for millions of years. But the river has a long journey to make before it gets to the sea. On its way to the sea the river passes through a lot of land. As it does so it picks up rocks and soil. The rocks and soil contain things called minerals. One of these minerals is salt.

It has taken millions of years for the rivers to drop enough salt in the sea to make it salty. This is why river water does not taste salty. Lake water does not taste salty either because as soon as one river brings some salt to the lake another river carries it out again!

We cannot drink sea water, not because it doesn't taste nice but because it would be bad for us. Because there is such a large supply of sea water in the world it would be very useful if we could find a way to take the salt out of it.

Scientists are working on this project at the moment. They have found many ways of taking the salt out of sea water. However, they need to find the cheapest way possible of doing so.

A **Copy or trace the picture of the river's journey to the sea.**

Write these labels on your picture in the correct places.

| The river starts here. | The river ends here. | The soil contains salt. |

| The river passes through land. | The river picks up rocks and soil. |

 B **Find these words in 'The Salty Sea'.**

million   mineral

Write down what you think the words mean.
- Now look up the words in a dictionary like this:
  Look up m first. Under m, look up mi.
  Then look up mi and the next letter, until you find the word.
  Which word will come first, mineral or million? How do you know?
  Read what the words mean in the dictionary. How close were you?
- Find two more words in 'The Salty Sea' that you are not sure of.
  Look them up in a dictionary.

C **Answer these questions.**

1. Write down the name of a mineral.
2. Why is the sea salty?
3. Why don't rivers taste salty?
4. Why doesn't lake water taste salty?
5. When would it be alright to drink sea water?

 D **Read this, from 'The Rime of the Ancient Mariner' by Samuel Taylor Coleridge.**

'Water, water everywhere,
Nor any drop to drink.'
- Can you guess what the water is and why?

31

A **Read these words. They all have the same sound.**

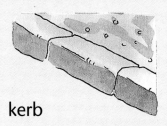

kerb

first

turkey

B **Now write these words in the correct lists and say them.**

girl

nurse

shirt

curl

perfume

C **Read these sentences. Add the er, ir and ur words to your list from B.**

1. Her sister would not buy a fur coat.

2. We were pleased to go to her birthday party.

D **Read these rhymes with a friend. Find the er, ir and ur words and add these to your lists.**

Over the bridge, under the sea,
Thirteen blackbirds
Swirl around the tree.

Thirty dirty turnips,
Stir them in the pan,
Turn around,
Twirl around,
And clap your hands.

E **Use some of the words in your lists to write your own rhyme.**

A <u>Split the compound words into smaller words.</u>

snowman = snow + man

ladybird =

handbag =

rainbow =

farmhouse =

pancake =

bedtime =

birthday =

B <u>Match the words below to make
larger words. Use the picture clues.</u>

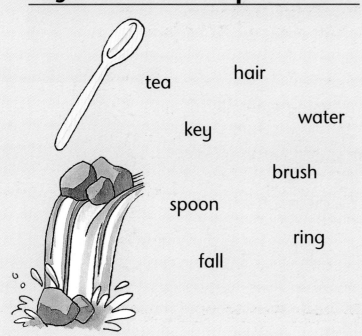

tea

key

spoon

fall

hair

water

brush

ring

Read these words and tell yourself what they mean.

tidy   do   happy   fold   like   able   fit   kind

 Read these sentences.

My room is tidy and clean.
My room is untidy because my toys are on the floor.

un in front of a word can mean not.
Put **un** in front of the words in A and write them down.
Now tell your friend what the new words mean.

 Read these words and tell yourself what they mean.

trust   honest   cover   please   agree

dis can also mean not.
Put **dis** in front of the words and write them down.
Tell your friend what they mean.

 Link each word with the correct sentence.
Explain to your friend what each word means.

Words	Sentences
1. disturb	Jane thought the eggs smelled very bad.
2. display	Polly kept stopping Sammy from working.
3. disgust	Ali showed his picture to the class.

Test each other on the spelling of the words.

 Find out the difference between unlike and dislike.

Verbs

- A verb is an action word. It tells us what a person, place or thing is doing, e.g. The lion **roars**. The village **is** lovely. Karen **runs** home.

 A **Write out these sentences, inserting the correct verb.**

1. The monkey *(laughs, swings, walks)* from branch to branch.
2. The elephant *(tiptoed, crashed, skipped)* through the jungle.
3. Paris *(was, flows, tumbles)* full of tourists.
4. We *(was, did, are, is)* in Germany.
5. The unhappy prisoner *(giggled, neighed, sobbed)*.
6. The school *(were, has, was, is)* pupils.
7. *(Eat, Gobble, Drink, Tickle)* your milk.

 B **Write out the sentences and underline the verbs.**

Last year we went on a school tour to France. We had a fantastic time. I brought back presents for all my family. We travelled to Paris and saw the Eiffel Tower. I loved France and some day I will return.

 C **Write out the sentences, inserting the correct verb.**

1. The tired old frog *(roars, purrs, croaks, neighs)* aloud.
2. The huge tiger *(squeaks, roars, bleats)* with hunger.
3. The spiteful hen *(quacks, cackles, chatters)* with glee.
4. The swooping seagull *(bellowed, screamed)* with pleasure.
5. The angry bull *(chirped, growled, bellowed)* with rage.

D **Write out these sentences. Put in your own verb.**

1. The long snake _____ along through the leaves of the forest.
2. The clumsy elephant _____ into the cool water.
3. The dainty butterfly _____ from petal to petal.
4. The frightened sheep _____ through the field.
5. The warm milk _____ from the baby's mouth.

35

I am, You are

A **Tom got his words mixed up.**
Write out the sentences correctly for him.

1. I is going to the park today.
2. The children am pleased with their new toys.
3. We is so happy to see my sister's new baby.
4. We is a happy family.
5. I loves to listen to pop music.
6. My Uncle Fred are always going fishing.
7. My Auntie Kay say she am fed up with Fred and his fishing.
8. My brother are a good cook.
9. My mum are a better one.
10. Those dogs is barking again!

B **Finish these sentences in your book about yourself and your friends.**

1. I live ...
2. I like ...
3. I dislike ...
4. We go ...
5. We love ...
6. My friends ...
7. We ...
8. My ...

Seesaw

 Read this. It is about something happening. It is in the present time which we call the present tense.

When I go to the park I do lots of things.
I see the ducks on the pond.
I hear the birds in the trees.
I go on the slide.
I skip with my friend.

 Now read this. It tells you that something has happened. It is in the past time or past tense.

When I went to the park I did lots of things.
I saw the ducks on the pond.
I heard the birds in the trees.
I went on the slide.
I skipped with my friend.

 Write down all the past and present tenses from A and B like this.

Present	Past
I go	I went
I see	...

 When we write a story or diary we write in the past tense. Finish this diary.

Yesterday, I caught a cold ...

Write three or more sentences.

The Pine Tree

A little pine tree stood in the great forest. It had lovely green needles which shone brightly in the sun. But the pine tree was not happy.

"I wish I had real leaves," grumbled the unhappy tree. "Then I would be as beautiful as any other tree in the forest! I wish I had leaves of gold."

Now it just so happened that a very kind fairy heard the pine tree. She waved her magic wand and the following morning the little tree had leaves of gold!

The golden leaves shone in the sunshine and when the wind blew they sounded like bells. However, a robber came by and heard the golden leaves tinkling.

"Ha! Ha!" he said. "I have found a golden treasure."

He picked all the leaves and soon the little pine tree was bare.

"People are greedy for gold," sighed the poor pine tree. "Maybe glass leaves would be better."

So the little fairy touched the tree and the following morning it had leaves of glass. However, as soon as the wind began to blow, all the shining glass leaves were broken. Once again the pine tree was bare.

"I wish I had green leaves," grumbled the tree. "Robbers wouldn't steal them and they wouldn't break either."

The kind fairy gave the tree fresh green leaves and for a short while it was content. However, soon a goat came along. "What juicy green leaves," he thought. "And such a little tree. I can reach every leaf!"

The hungry goat ate every single leaf on the tree until once again it was completely bare.

"Oh dear, oh dear," cried the tree. "Maybe green leaves are fine for big trees but I wish I could have my needles back again. Robbers do not steal them, the wind does not break them and goats do not eat them."

Next morning the needles were back. The tree shook them in the sun. It let the wind make music with them.

"These are the best kind of leaves," laughed the tree and it was never unhappy again.

A Who was in the story? Write down the correct names from the list. Write two sentences about one of them.

the oak tree   the pine tree   a cruel fairy   a kind fairy
the robber   the storm   the wind   the goat

B Write out and finish these sentences.

1. The pine tree was unhappy with gold leaves because ...
2. The pine tree was unhappy with glass leaves because ...
3. The pine tree was unhappy with green leaves because ...
4. The pine tree wanted its pine needles back because ...

C Answer these questions.

1. Where did the pine tree live?
2. If the pine tree lived in a garden, how might the story be different?

D Write down what you think this means.

The wind made music with the pine needles.

E Write the story about the pine tree in your own words.

Begin: once upon a time ...

Speech Marks

A **Read what the pine tree says in the speech bubble.**

When we read a book we know someone is speaking because we see speech marks.

B **Copy out what the pine tree says.**
Write it in speech marks as shown.

"I wish I had green leaves."

C **Read these speech bubbles. Write down the words in speech marks.**

D **Who is speaking? Write down their names.**

E **Find speech marks in the story on page 38.**

The Sentence

- A sentence begins with a capital letter and ends with a full stop.
- A sentence is a set of words that makes sense.

 Are the words below sentences? Write 'yes' or 'no' for each. If you write 'no', write a correct sentence.

1. My poor dog is very sick.
2. I have a large green.
3. The ball is over there beside the tree.
4. In the middle of the street.
5. The sun is blazing down.
6. Over to the left.
7. The fish swam.
8. He ran away from.

 The words below are sentences. Can you make them more 'interesting'? The first one is done for you.

1. The wolf came by. The hungry wolf seemed to appear from nowhere.
2. The shark attacked.
3. The music is nice.
4. The wind blew.
5. The skunk arrived.
6. The eagle flew.
7. The leaves fell.

 Write two interesting sentences about the picture.

Stone Age Adventure

A **This is a title for a story. Use the ideas below to help you write it.**

Now, you are going to work out a plan for your story. A plan is just an 'outline' for your story – a few words or sentences to help you write the real thing.

1. Write down all the words that come into your head when you read the title, e.g. boar, calves, apes, wild animals, fire, Flintstones, bears, wolves.

2. **Where will your story take place?** In a forest? In a wood? By the sea? Near a lake? In a cave? It's your story. You decide.

3. **What 'characters' or people will be in your story?** A mother? A father? A granny? A pet boar (who goes wild!)? A snake? Someone from the future? A Stone Age rock band? A teacher? A stray dinosaur? You decide.

4. **What will happen in the story?** Does someone from the Stone Age end up in the future? Does the pet boar fall in love with a wild boar? Does the Stone Age band become famous? Does another 'tribe' try to take over? You decide. Anything can happen. It's your story.

5. **What will happen at the end of your story?** Do you move into a new cave? Do you get a new skin for the winter? Does the person from the future stay in the past? Do you make friends with the new tribe?

6. Now write your full story, 'Stone Age Adventure'. Good Luck!

Using Commas

Nina is going on holiday. Here is the list of what she is taking.

dress
skirt
jumper
coat
toothbrush
comic

She could write her list using commas like this:
I will take a dress, a skirt, a jumper, a coat, a toothbrush and a comic.

 A **This is what Nina has in her school bag.**
Write out the list using commas.

book
pen
pencil
rubber
ruler

Begin: In her bag Nina has a book ...

 B **Using commas, write down some of the things:**

- in your bag
- in your classroom
- in the playground
- in your room at home
- you buy when you go shopping.

C **Read your lists to your friend.**

The Goat, the Wolf and the Cabbages

Long ago, a young man lived beside a river. He owned a small boat and he made his living by taking people and their goods across the river. However, his boat was so small that he could only carry one person or one load of goods at a time.

One day he was asked to carry three things across the river – a wolf, a sack of cabbages and a goat. He could only carry one thing at a time. This would mean leaving two things behind on the river bank. He could come back for the other two things but what would happen while he was away?

If he took the wolf across and left the goat and the cabbages, the goat would eat the cabbages. If he took the cabbages, the wolf would eat the goat.

If he took the goat across first and left the wolf and the cabbages, the wolf would not eat the cabbages. But what would happen when he carried the wolf or the cabbages over to where the goat was? While he went back across to get the last thing, either the wolf would eat the goat or the goat would eat the cabbages.

After a lot of thought the man finally worked it out. He was able to get the wolf, the goat and the cabbages safely across the river. Can you work it out? If not, the answer is written upside down.

First he took the goat across the river. Then he went back and brought the cabbages over. Then instead of leaving the goat and the cabbages together, he brought the goat back across the river again and left the cabbages behind. When he got to the other side where the wolf was he took the wolf into the boat and took the goat out. He left the goat behind and carried the wolf over to where the cabbages were. He left the wolf with the cabbages and went back over for the goat!

A **Answer these questions.**

    1. Where did the young man live?
    2. How did he make his living?
    3. What was the problem with his boat?
    4. One day he was asked to take three things. What were they?

B **Key phrases.**

Write down key phrases from paragraphs 2, 3 and 4 which will help you explain the problem the young man had in carrying the goat, wolf and cabbages across the river.

Begin like this:
Paragraph 1. If he took the wolf ...

C **Use the key phrases to write out the man's problem, in your own words.**

D **Now write down how the man solved the problem. Use your own words.**

Begin by writing down key phrases like this:

First he ...

Then he ...

When you have written it down, explain it to a friend.

Change the Story

 A **Write a story.**

You have read the story 'The Goat, the Wolf and the Cabbages'. Now you are going to write the same story but with three different things. (You must write the story in your own words.)

You can choose any three things but two of them will be enemies like the wolf and the goat or one might eat the other like the goat and the cabbages. You could choose a lion, an antelope and a sack of green leaves. You could choose a dog, a cat and a mouse. It's your story so you can choose anything you like!

Draw a picture for your story.

 B **Read the story.**

Now read a friend's story. What different things did they use? Did you choose any the same? Find out if anyone else in the class used one of the same 'enemies' as you did.

Silent e

A **Read the words below. Add 'silent e' and then read the word again.**

cap_   can_   tap_   mat_   pan_

B **Unscramble these letters to make words. The first one is done for you. The 'silent e' always comes at the end.**

1. epal = pale   **2.** gaem =   **3.** amfle =   **4.** egat =

5. afme =   **6.** embla =   **7.** etal =   **8.** emca =

9. etapl =   **10.** meal =   **11.** adem =   **12.** erasc =

13. etad =   **14.** cear =   **15.** evash =

C **Read these words. Add 'silent e' and read them again. Put them into sentences.**

rip_   pip_   fin_   rid_   fir_

D **Write the correct word for each picture.**

1	2	3	4
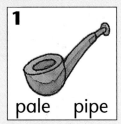			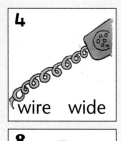
pale pipe	like hike	ride rice	wire wide

5	6	7	8

broke bike	tame time	fine fire	hide hive

9	10	11	12

smile snake	win wine	tile tale	hike kite

The Camel's Complaint

Canary-birds feed on sugar and seed,
Parrots have crackers to crunch;
And as for the poodles, they tell me the noodles
Have chicken and cream for their lunch.
But there's never a question
About my digestion –
Anything does for me.

Cats, you're aware, can repose in a chair,
Chickens can roost upon rails;
Puppies are able to sleep in a stable,
And oysters can slumber in pails.
But no one supposes
A poor camel dozes –
Any place does for me.

Lambs are enclosed where it's never exposed,
Coops are constructed for hens;
Kittens are treated to houses well heated,
And pigs are protected by pens.
But a camel comes handy
Wherever it's sandy –
Anywhere does for me.

People would laugh if you rode a giraffe,
Or mounted the back of an ox;
It's nobody's habit to ride on a rabbit,
Or try to bestraddle a fox.
But as for a camel, he's
Ridden by families –
Any load does for me.

A snake is as round as a hole in the ground,
And weasels are wavy and sleek;
And no alligator could ever be straighter
Than lizards that live in a creek.
But a camel's all lumpy
And bumpy and humpy –
Any shape does for me.

Charles E. Carryl

48

A **Write down the words you think fit the poem from the list below.**

funny	sad	slow	bouncy	frightening
verse	long	short	rhyme	thoughtful

Add two more words of your own which fit the poem.

 B **Write about the main animal in the poem as shown below.**

The main animal in the poem is ...
It is sorry for itself because ...
In the last verse the poet says its shape is ...

 C **Look at the rhymes in the poem.**

1. Find the words that rhyme with the following:
crunch, rails, hens, ox, sleek

2. Write down two lines that rhyme at the end of a verse.

3. Read this line: A snake is as round as a hole in the ground.
The middle of the line rhymes with the end of the rhyme.
Find another line that does this and read it aloud.

 D **Make up your own rhymes.**

1. Find animals in the poem and make up your own rhymes to go with them, like this:
Parrots love carrots
Poodles can doodle

2. Make up descriptions of animals where the letters are the same at the beginning of each word, like this:
Crunching crocodiles
Little lambs

The Full Stop

● A sentence ends with a full stop.

 The full stops and capital letters are missing from these sentences. Rewrite them.

1. the cat is on the roof
2. the fish is in the bath
3. today is christmas day
4. my sister's name is ann
5. i love mondays
6. my birthday is in may
7. we are going to england

 Write some sentences about each picture.

 Finish these sentences.

1. The furry bat
2. The crashing wave
3. They laughed
4. The ghost

Copy the correct picture.

| swing | sling | wall | holly |

 Choose the correct word for each sentence.

1. I was *(stuck, stung, sting, stick)* by a bee.

2. I was *(winning, running, robbing)* too fast and I fell.

3. I *(hunt, hill, hung)* my wet shirt on the line.

4. The rat has a very *(lorry, lot, long, lost)* tail.

5. The man is *(mowing, milking, talking)* the cow.

6. I am *(tricking, walking, packing)* my bag.

7. There are six boys and girls in my *(gong, gang, fang)*.

8. This hat is too *(small, stall, smack, sting)* for me.

9. My sister is very *(till, tall, tell, talk)*.

10. My dad is *(falling, cutting, calling, digging)* me.

C **Choose words from the box for the sentences below.**

| baby | sixty | sty | pity | sunny | angry | rusty | fly |
| happy | try | sandy | dry | granny | cry | nappy |

1. I have a _____ sister who is very _____ .

2. The pig is in the _____ .

3. I will _____ to pass my test. It would be a _____ if I didn't.

4. We are on a _____ beach and it is a _____ day.

5. I am _____ because my dress is not _____ .

6. My _____ is _____ today.

7. The baby is going to _____ because its _____ is wet.

8. The _____ is going to land on the _____ old bike.

Hibernation

How would you like to go to sleep in the autumn and wake up in the spring? You could sleep through all the nasty cold weather that these months bring. (But don't forget you'd have to miss Christmas because you'd be asleep!)

One animal that sleeps from autumn to spring is the hedgehog. It doesn't sleep in the way we do at night. Its heart slows down and nearly stops. Its breathing almost stops as well. When it is awake its body is warm, so it is known as a warm-blooded animal. When it goes into its winter sleep its body grows cold. We call this winter sleep hibernation.

The hedgehog is not the only animal that hibernates. Bats, mice, chipmunks, bears and skunks also hibernate. Snakes, frogs and toads hibernate as well.

One of the best-known hibernators is the little dormouse. In autumn it works hard to build up its stores of body fat. It then settles down into its winter nest, usually among tree roots. Its heart slows down to only one beat every few minutes. Its body temperature also becomes as low as the temperature outside its nest.

The winter sleep of some animals is not as deep as others'. The bear's body temperature drops but its heartbeat hardly changes at all. This means that if the weather gets warmer the bear can wake itself up. Because of all the fat it has stored it doesn't need to eat. So if you meet a bear in winter it's unlikely that you'll end up as its breakfast!

Have you ever wondered why some animals hibernate? The answer is that many warm-blooded animals need extra energy in order to stay warm in winter. They usually get this energy from food but in the cold winter months there is very little food to be found. Some animals solve this problem by migrating to a warmer place but many others hibernate instead.

Perhaps someday humans will be given a choice for the winter months. Hibernate or migrate? Which would you do?

A **Match 1 2 3 4 with a b c d.**

1. hibernate   **2.** migrate   **3.** energy   **4.** temperature
a. the amount of heat or cold
b. to be strong and active
c. when animals sleep in winter
d. when animals go to warmer places for winter

B **Write down a list of animals that hibernate.**

Begin: 1.
        2.

C **Make a diagram about the dormouse. Start like this.**

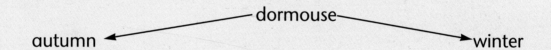

dormouse

autumn   winter

Write on your diagram what the dormouse does in autumn and winter.

D **Copy the correct sentence.**

1. The bear never wakes up in winter.
2. The bear only wakes up when it's cold
3. The bear always wakes up in winter.
4. The bear can wake itself up if the weather gets warmer.
Add 'because' to your sentence and give an answer.

E **Answer these questions.**

1. Why do some animals migrate? Write down your answer. Begin:
    Some animals migrate because ...
2. Why do some animals hibernate? Write down the answer in your
    own words.

Adventure on the High Seas

 Talk about it.

What do you think is going to happen in this picture? Who is on board each ship? Is there going to be a battle? Who will win? Will a ship sink? Before you begin, make a list of the words that came into your head when you read the title.

> sharks   sails   roaring   cutlass   sword   dagger
> crashing waves   battle   pirates

 Write the story.

Think carefully **before** you begin to write. Make a rough **plan** first if you wish. (Looking back at page 42 will help you.) Then begin.

A Stone Age Man

 Read this passage about a Stone Age man.

At first the man did not hear the boar coming towards him. Suddenly a huge crashing noise told him it was near by. He tried to forget his fears as he faced the angry beast. He raised his spear and drove it into the animal. He aimed well. His family would not go hungry.

 Look for the words that have ear in them.
Read them again. Write them down.

hear ...

 Choose the correct ea word for each sentence.

1. I banged my *(head/hear)* on the wall.
2. I cried when I found out that my fish was *(dead/deal)*.
3. After I *(rest/read)* 'Matilda' I wanted to see the film.
4. I always *(dried/dread)* going to see my grumpy auntie.
5. My dad told me not to *(tread/tried)* in the mud.
6. I like to *(spread/spring)* jam on my *(brow/bread)*.

 Read the words you have written for C.

Question Marks

● A question ends with a question mark.

 Copy out the sentences and add question marks (?). Start a new line and write the answers.

1. Where do you live
2. What is your name
3. Do you have a sister
4. Do you have a pet
5. How old are you
6. When is your birthday
7. What is your favourite food

 Choose a word from the box. Put in the question marks.

How	What	Why	Is	Where	Does	Who

1. _____ your father know you are here
2. _____ is your sick parrot
3. _____ time is your bus due
4. _____ is your house
5. _____ do you think you are trying to fool
6. _____ did you do that
7. _____ that the way you behave at home

C Write questions for these answers.

1. Leaves fall in autumn.
2. Winter is a cold season.
3. March has 31 days.
4. Each season has three months.
5. There are 30 days in June.
6. St Andrew's Day is in November.

A **The capital letters are missing from these sentences. Rewrite them with the capital letters.**

1. it was sunday evening before i remembered tom's birthday.
2. my cousin jack said that he was going to florida in july.
3. carlos, my penfriend from spain, said that he'd be coming for christmas.
4. fluffy, our dog, disappeared on tuesday but returned on friday.
5. i left africa in december and headed for india.
6. doctor carter is coming from america on wednesday.

 B **Make one sentence from each set of four nouns.**

1. Kate	France	skunk	aeroplane
2. Sam	crocodile	bath	towel
3. snake	garden	worm	grass
4. Tom	tiger	jungle	house

C **Write the missing question mark (?) or full stop.**

1. Did you see that film that was on last night
2. I thought that Carol was going to the park
3. How did you get on with Shenaz
4. What time will you be at the bus stop
5. I will never speak to you again
6. May I borrow your pencil

 D **Choose the correct verb (action word) for each sentence.**

1. My teeth (*shrank, grew, sparkled*) after I brushed them.
2. My mum (*dragged, drove, carried*) the car down the road.
3. My dad (*ate, swallowed, read, licked*) the magazine.
4. Tim (*purred, brayed, slept, bleated*) in his cot.
5. The elephant (*sucked, woke, pulled*) the water up.
6. The binman (*tasted, gobbled, emptied*) the rubbish.
7. The bird (*jumped, flew, galloped, wobbled*) over the roof.
8. The snake (*ran, slithered, cried*) under the rock.

Flags

The history of the flag goes back about 5000 years and the sight of their country's flag has always had a strong effect on people. Today flags are still used in wars but they are also used in peacetime. They are used in many different ways: to send messages, to greet the winner of a race, to wave at football matches.

A flag is a piece of cloth with a special pattern and colour. One edge is fixed to a pole and the rest of it flaps in the wind. Flags can be any shape but they are usually rectangular. The long rope used to raise the flag is called the halyard.

Differently coloured flags mean different things. Waving a white flag means that you come in peace or that you wish to surrender. In motor racing, waving a red flag means that the driver should stop. Waving a black flag means that the driver must make a 'pit stop' to get wheels changed or the car checked. A yellow and red striped flag means there is oil on the track.

Before the telephone and radio were invented, flags were used to send messages. One of the earliest uses of flags was to send messages at sea. There was a special flag for each letter of the alphabet and for each number. Today these 'signal flags' are hardly ever used.

Copy the flags on this page. Use the colour guide to colour them in.
1 = green; 2 = white; 3 = orange; 4 = blue; 5 = red; 6 = yellow.

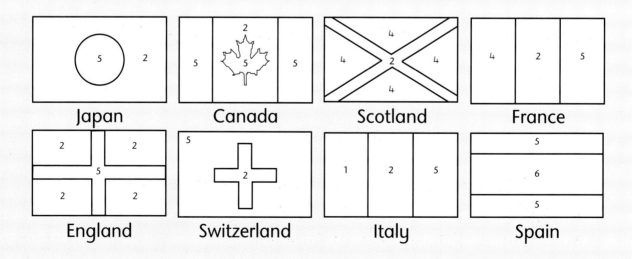

A Write down the answers to these questions and the paragraphs where you found the information.

1. What is a flag?
2. How far back does the history of the flag go?
3. Why were flags waved during battle?
4. When are flags used in peacetime?

B Write down what different coloured flags mean.

Give your writing a main heading like this:
What Differently Coloured Flags Mean

Add sub-headings like this:
The White Flag

C Answer these questions.

1. How did people send messages using flags?
2. When would it be difficult to use flags to send messages? Think of two occasions.
3. Why don't we use signal flags today?

D What else would you like to know about flags?

Write down three questions.

E Choose the correct word for each sentence.

1. The (*site, sight*) of their flag has a strong effect on people.
2. Flags are used in (*piece, peace*) time.
3. Flags are used in wartime (*two, too*).

A Flag Tells its Story

 A **Write about it.**

You are a flag! Choose one of the scenes from above and write your story. Are you a flag at a match? Do you find yourself beside a flag from another country? Are you feeling sick from being waved about so much? Is your head aching? Is the sun ruining your colours? Is the wind trying to pull you off your pole or stick? Are you a white flag – about to surrender? Do you make the rider change his/her mind about surrendering? Are you on top of Mount Everest being shoved into the cold snow? Have you just signalled the end of a race?

First, write down all the 'flag' words that come into your head.

surrender	blowing	hoisted	waved
cheering	squashed	billowing	galloping

Write a rough plan of your story. Then begin!

The Same Words

Sometimes words look the same but do not sound the same.

 Look at the picture and say the word.

tear   bow   lead   row

tear   bow   lead   row

 Write down these sentences, putting in the missing word. Use the words in A. Read the sentences.

1. A large _____ fell from her eye.

2. I have another _____ in my old jeans.

3. My sister wears a _____ in her hair.

4. The dancer made a _____ at the end of the dance.

5. The shopping bag was full and as heavy as _____ .

6. When I take Rover for a walk I put on his _____ .

7. If we visit the lake we always _____ the boats.

8. Two people were having a noisy _____ in the street.

C **Finish these sentences and write them down. Read them to a friend.**

1. I live _____ .

2. I will read _____ .

3. Jamie brought a live snake _____ .

4. Last night I read a story about _____ .

Underline the words that look the same but do not sound the same.

Endings

Sometimes we add ly to make new words.
Come on Bill, don't be slow. This tells us what Bill is like.

The time seemed to pass so slowly. This tells us how the time passed.

We can make all sorts of new words by adding endings.

help/helpful   fast/fastest   rest/restless

 A **Read these words and write down all those with ly, ful, est and less endings.**

kitchen	tea	cake	suddenly
jam	bee	painful	loudest
lump	ugly	cry	restless
arm	endless	hurt	careful
nearest	better	bravely	happy

Underline the endings.

 B **Read this sentence.**

I was in the kitchen eating cake when suddenly a bee flew through the window.

Write three more sentences. Use the words in A with the endings ly, ful, est and less.

All Together

 Choose the correct word and write the sentence.

He/She is jumping.   It/He is singing.   They/It is quacking. I/They are dancing.

 Read these sentences about the picture below.

Ruby is wearing her red dress and Dean is wearing his green jumper.
The cage is on its table. The children are in their classroom.

We say her for a girl or woman and his for a boy or man. We say its
for a thing and their for a group.

Write five more sentences about the picture.
Use the words his, her, its and their.

The Fairies

1

Up the airy mountain,
  Down the rushy glen,
We daren't go a-hunting
  For fear of little men;
Wee folk, good folk,
  Trooping all together;
Green jacket, red cap,
  And white owl's feather!

2

Down along the rocky shore,
  Some make their home,
They live on crispy pancakes
  Of yellowtide-foam;
Some in the reeds
  Of the black mountain lake,
With frogs for their watch-dogs,
  All night awake.

3

By the craggy hill side,
  Through the mosses bare,
They have planted thorn-trees
  For pleasure here and there.
Is any man so daring
  As dig them up in spite,
He shall find their sharpest thorns
  In his bed at night.

4

Up the airy mountain,
  Down the rushy glen,
We daren't go a-hunting
  For fear of little men;
Wee folk, good folk,
  Trooping all together;
Green jacket, red cap,
  And white owl's feather!

William Allingham (adaptation)

A Talk about it.

- Do you think there might be little folk such as these about?
- Do you know any stories about fairies or one fairy? Tell the story.
- Would you dig up a thorn-tree? Why? Why not?
- Do these fairies sound like good ones or bad ones?
- What is each fairy doing? Describe the fairies. Describe the scenery.
- Do you like this poem? Why? Have you got a favourite poem?
- Do you think the author gives us a good description of the fairies?
- How does he do this? What words give us a clear picture?

B Activities.

- Clap your hands or tap your feet when saying the poem. Do you like the rhythm?
- Write a story or poem about a man who dug up one of the thorn-trees.